FINGERPRINT FUN

DINOSAURS

KATE DAUBNEY

ARCTURUS

ARCTURUS

This edition published in 2018 by Arcturus Publishing Limited
26/27 Bickels Yard, 151–153 Bermondsey Street,
London SE1 3HA

Illustrated by Kate Daubney
Written by William Potter
Edited by Susannah Bailey
Designed by Square and Circus

ISBN: 978-1-78428-984-3
CH005800NT
Supplier 29 Date 1217 Print run 6139

Printed in China

FiNGERPRiNTiNG iS FUN!

In this book, you'll learn how to paint your very own fingerprint dinosaurs. To do this, you'll need to use different parts of your fingers.

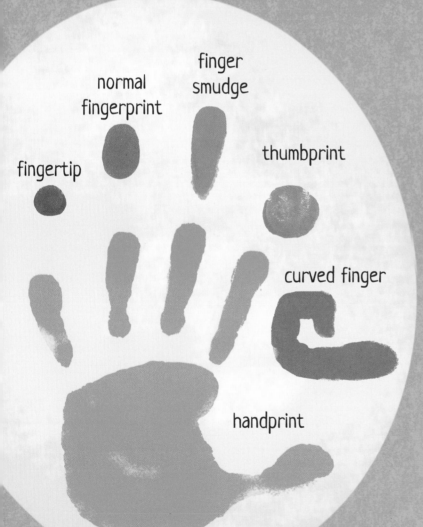

normal fingerprint

finger smudge

fingertip

thumbprint

curved finger

handprint

OUR TOP TiPS:

1. Make sure that you have a wet cloth or tissues nearby to change the paint on your finger.

2. Only add a tiny amount of water to your paints, or they'll become too runny.

3. Experiment with how much paint you put on your finger. The smaller the amount of paint, the quicker the print will dry!

4. Leave your prints to dry before you add any line work with a black pen.

5. You may find it easier to make some prints by turning the page around or upside down.

PLATED PLANT-EATER

Can you draw this cute dino?

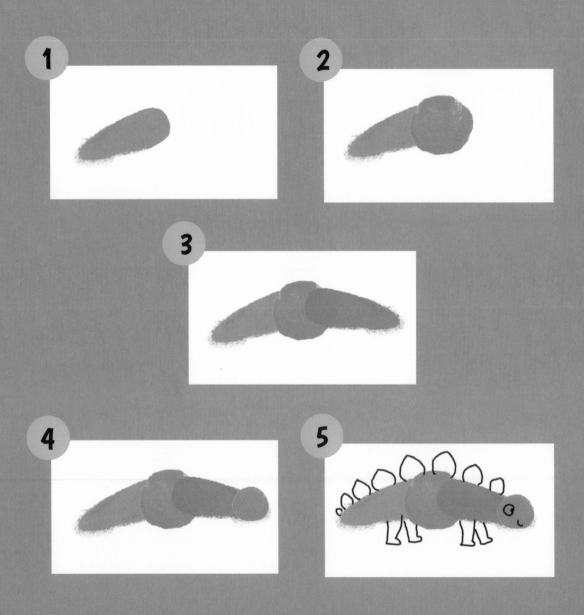

1

2

3

4

5

STEGOSAURUS (STEG-oh-SORE-us)

Print plates on the dinos' backs, then add smudges for spikes on the tip of their tails.

FLYING FISH-EATER

Use finger smudges for this flying reptile's long head and wings.

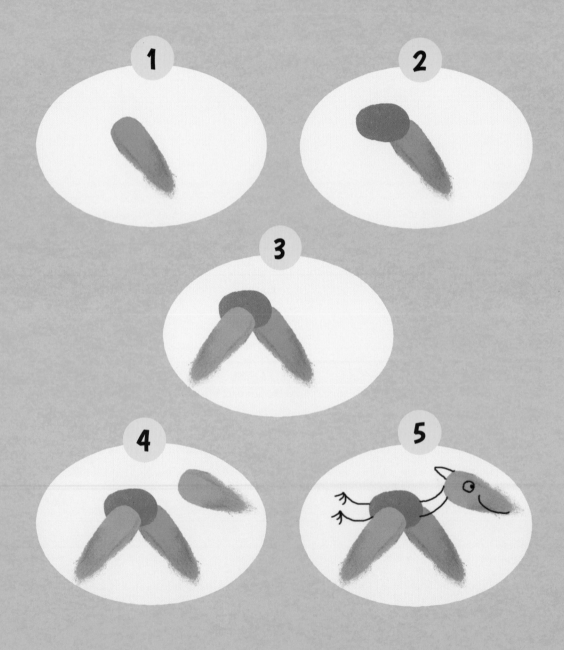

PTEROSAUR (TEH-roh-sore)

Help these pterosaurs catch a meal by printing yummy fish in their jaws.

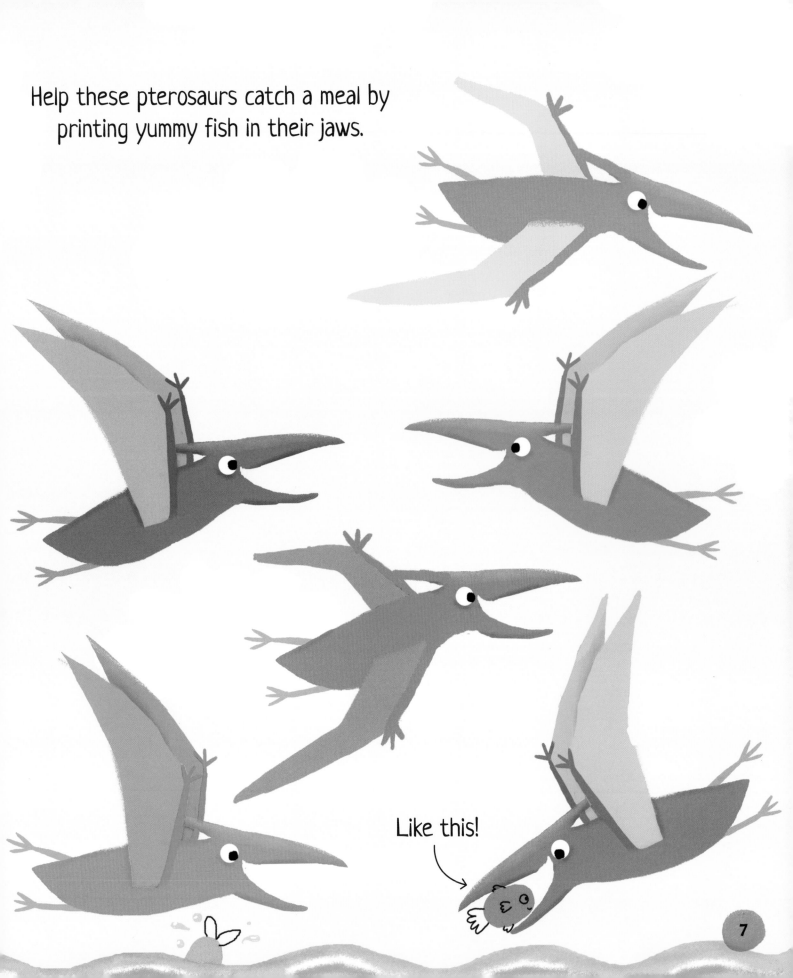

Like this!

GiGANTiC GLiDER

This giant flying reptile has come to rest.

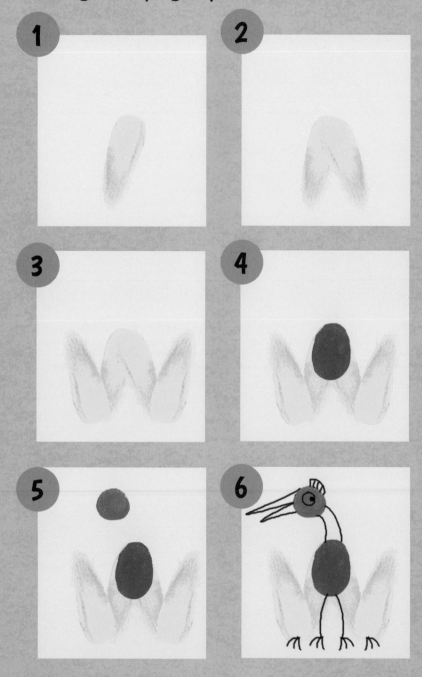

QUETZALCOATLUS (KWETS-ul-koh-AT-luss)

TOOTHY TERROR

Give scary Tyrannosaurus a jaw full of sharp teeth.

TYRANNOSAURUS (ty-RAN-oh-SORE-us REX)

SPINY HUNTER

Now, can you follow the steps to make a fierce T. rex?

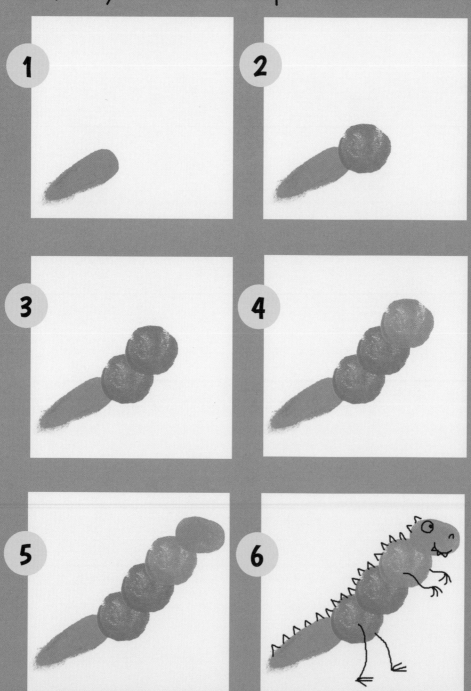

Add smudge spines along T. rex's back and fingertip spots on its body.

TOUGH GUY

Follow the steps to build this spiky dino.

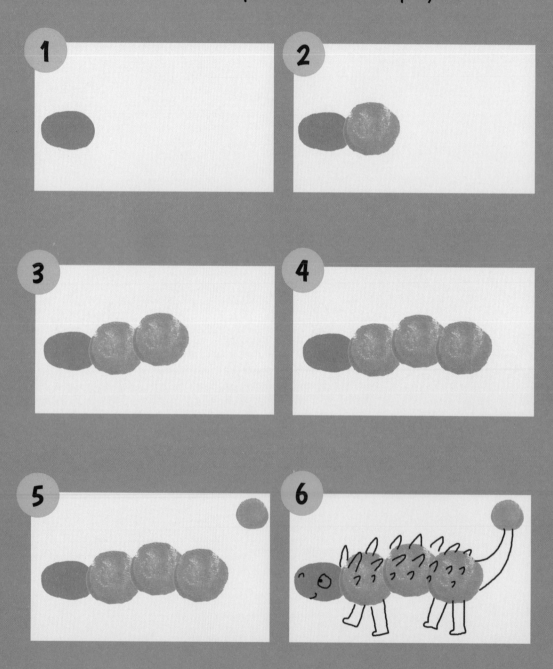

ANKYLOSAURUS (AN-kih-loh-SORE-us)

Use finger smudges to add spikes all over this dinosaur's back, plus two on its tail.

RUNNING RAPTOR

Can you use your finger and thumb to shape a dinosaur head?

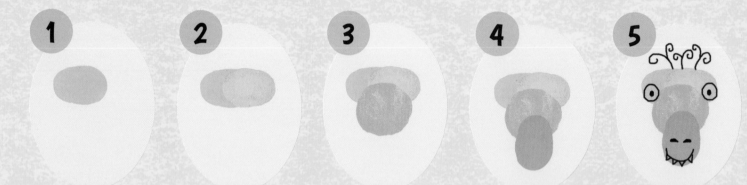

Paint this feathered dino with fingerprints and smudges.

VELOCIRAPTOR (veh-LOSS-ee-RAP-tuhr)

With many different paints, create a pattern of feathers on the back and arms of this fast-running hunter.

TREETOP TASTER

Paint this long-necked dinosaur with a row of fingerprints.

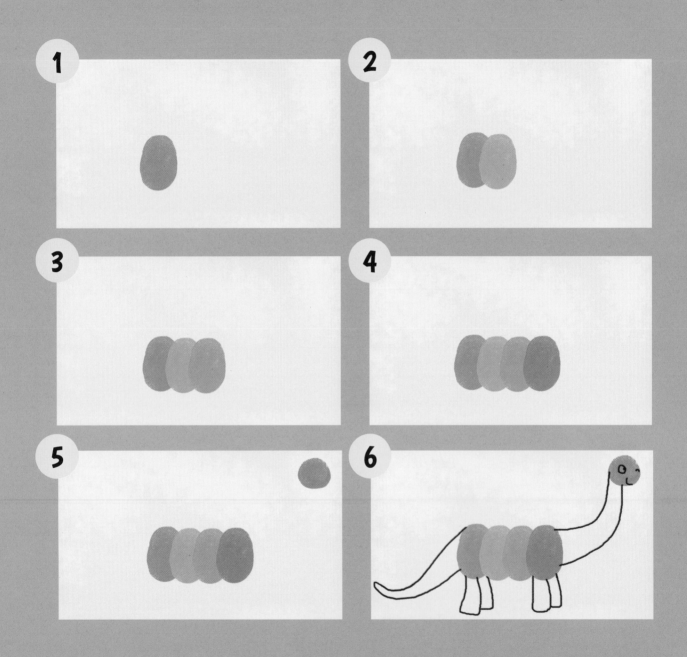

DIPLODOCUS (dih-PLOD-doh-kus)

Decorate Diplodocus with different shades of green paint.

HARD HEAD

Give this dino a fingertip head with a ring of spikes.

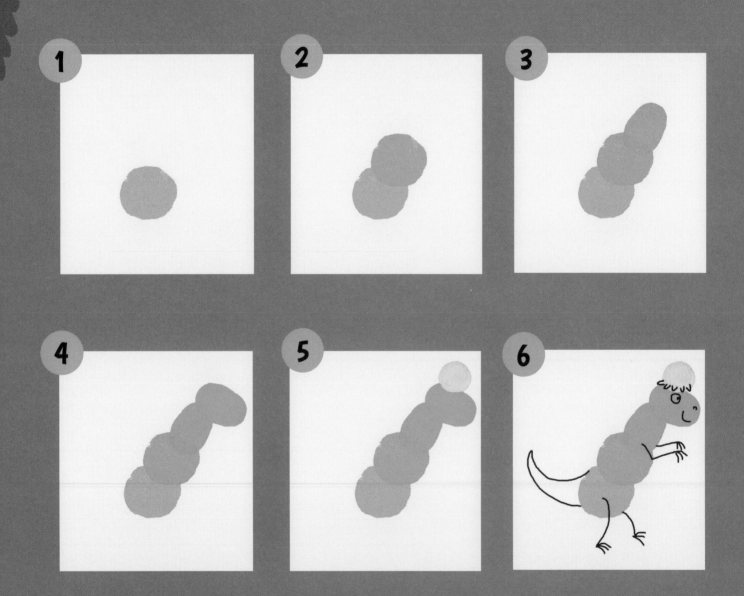

PACHYCEPHALOSAURUS (PACK-ee-SEF-ah-loh-SORE-us)

Add a tough dome to each of these creatures' heads.

DEEP DIVERS

This ocean critter has many body parts and tiny legs.

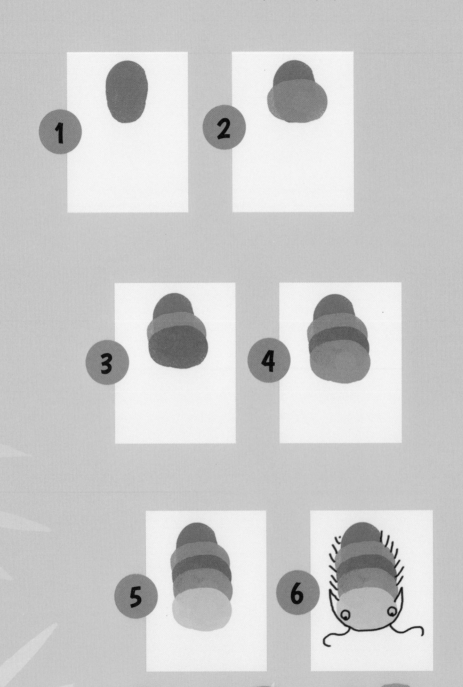

TRILOBITE (TRY-lo-bite)

Print lots of trilobites on the seabed.

BEAKY BITER

Start with a smudge tail to build a body for this big dino.

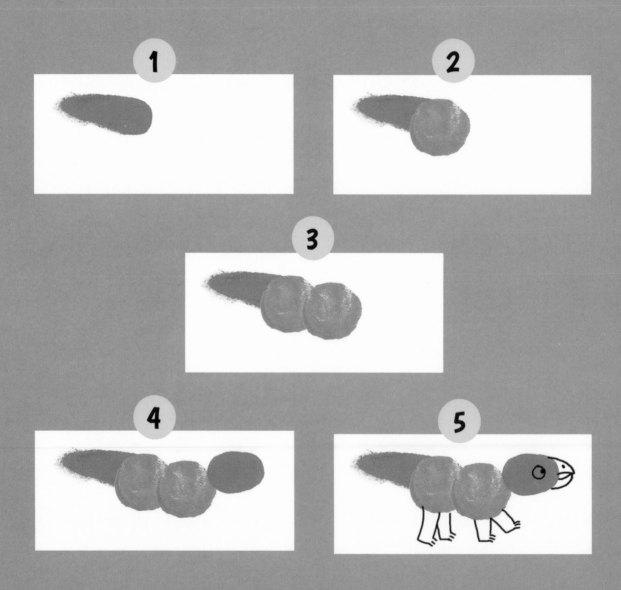

PLACERIAS (plah-SEE-ree-ass)

FABULOUS FRILLS

Paint a circle of fingerprints to decorate Triceratops' neck frill. Then, add smudges for horns.

TRICERATOPS (try-SEH-rah-tops)

CRESTED CREATURE

Join a handprint to a smudge to make a high-reaching plant-eater.

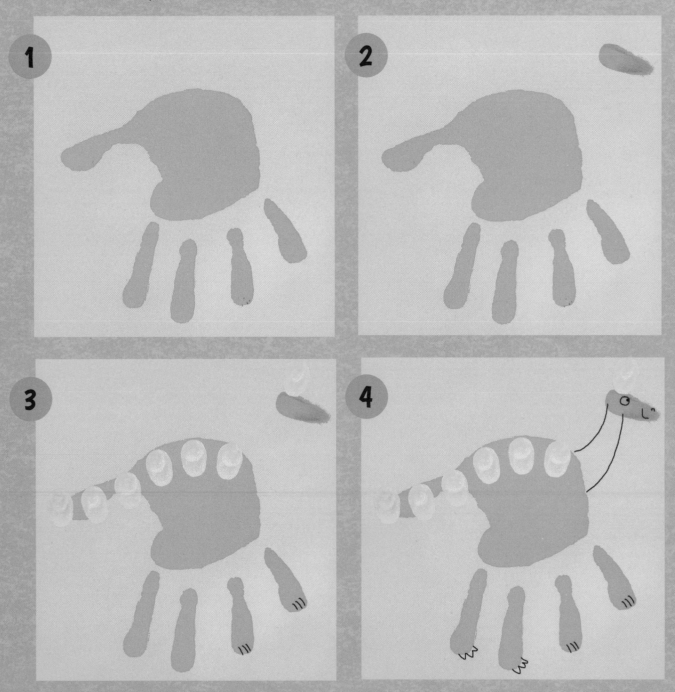

LAMBEOSAURUS (LAM-bee-oh-SORE-us)

Cover the tree with juicy green leaves for this pair of dinos to chew on.

BREAKING FREE

Print an egg, then a tiny dino head peeping out!

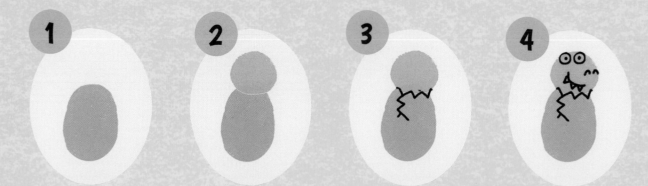

Now, add some more eggs that are beginning to crack open.

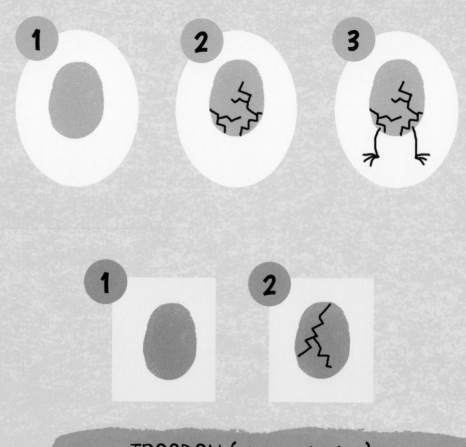

TROODON (TROH-oh-don)

Give the pair of Troodon some fingerprint eggs.
Then, draw their dino babies starting to hatch.

EARLY BiRD

Use smudges for wings and a tail on this bird.

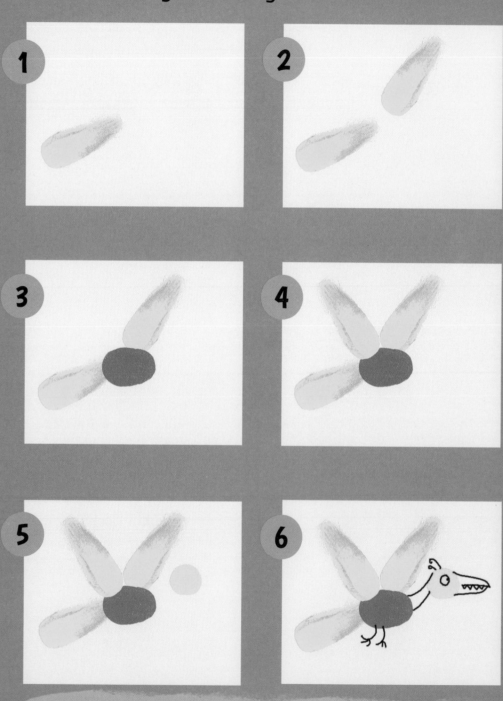

ARCHAEOPTERYX (ARK-ee-OPT-er-icks)

Print eye-catching fingerprints to give this first bird fantastic feathers!

SUPER SAIL

Paint a handprint with extra smudges for the sail on this reptile.

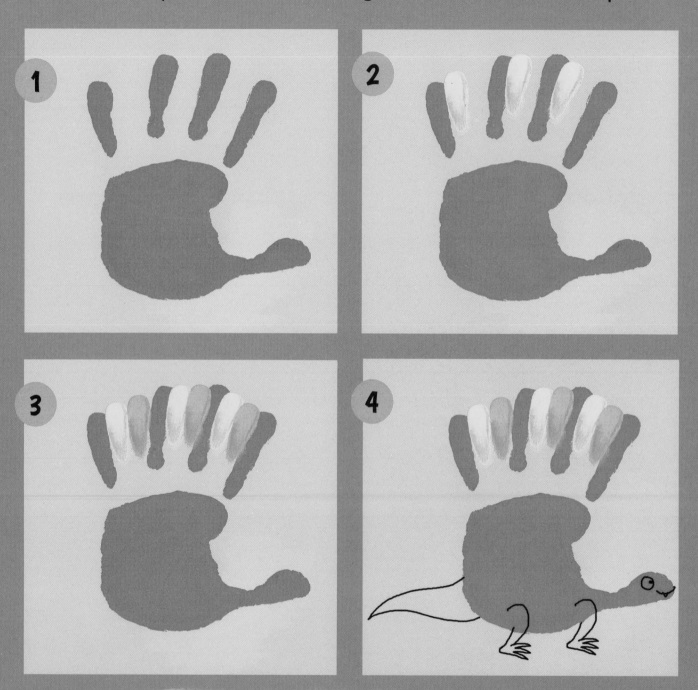

DIMETRODON (dy-MET-roh-don)

Use a row of bright finger smudges to
complete this dinosaur.

DARING DRAGONFLY

Can you make this early insect?

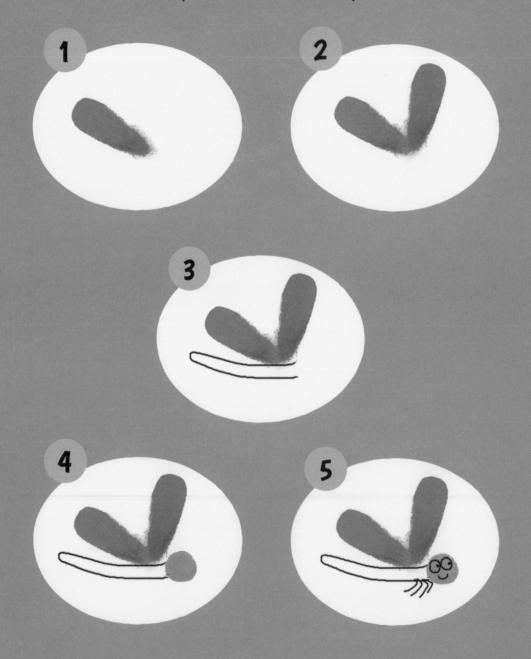

Now, paint several dragonflies buzzing around this prehistoric pond scene.

SHORESIDE SNAPPER

A line of prints and smudges creates this early crocodile!

1

2

3

4

5

PARASUCHUS
(pah-rah-SOOK-us)

6

Add some crocs to this sandy scene.

SWIRLY SHELL

Make a print with the side of your fist, then add a thumbprint to make this fossil shell.

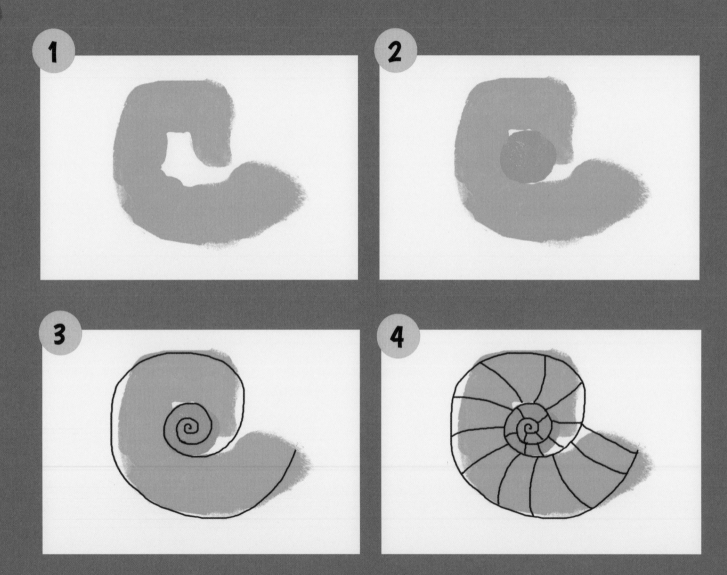

1

2

3

4

AMMONITE (AM-oh-nite)

PREHISTORIC PADDLER

Follow the steps to create this sea monster.

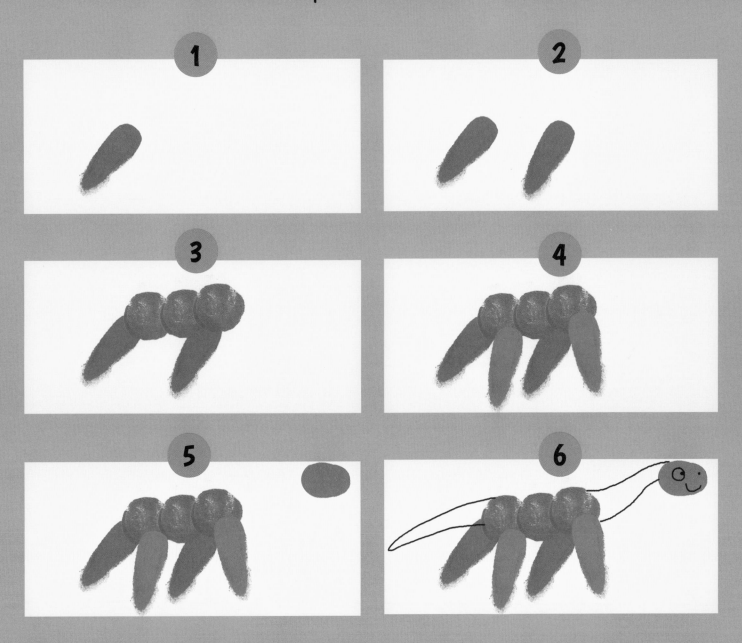

PLESIOSAURUS (PLEE-see-oh-SORE-us)

GRAZING GIANT

Build a row of prints to show a leaf-loving dinosaur!

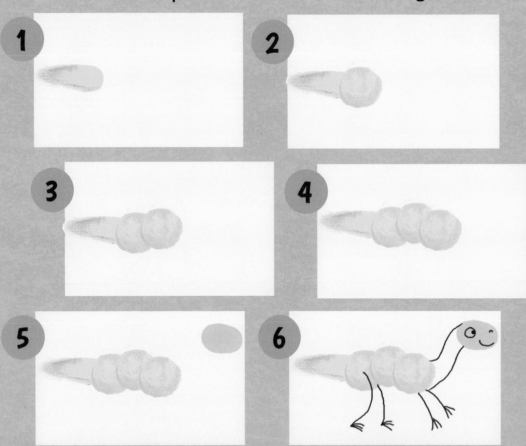

Here's how to make a leafy bush.

IGUANODON (ig-WAH-noh-don)

Decorate the dinos, then print some green bushes for them to munch on.

SPIKY STAR

This large plant-eater needs a spiky neck frill and horn.

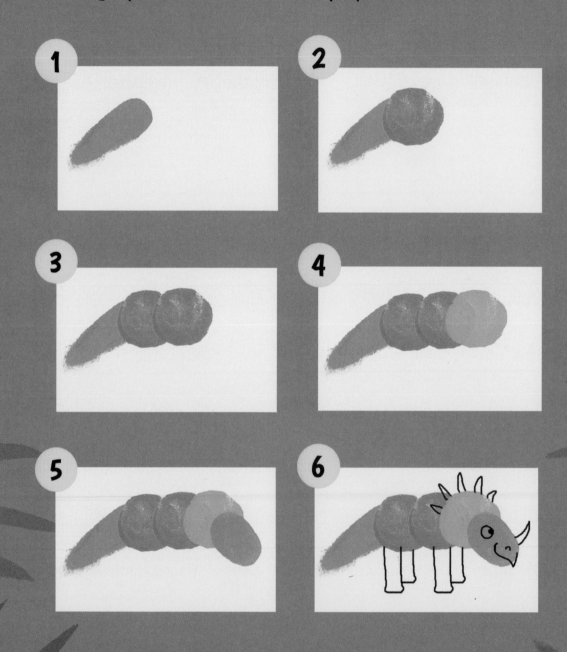

STYRACOSAURUS (sty-RACK-oh-SORE-us)

Add a rainbow of smudgy spikes around the frills on these dinosaurs.

PREHISTORIC PRINTS

Follow the steps to make this T. rex footprint.

Now, try a print for Triceratops (try-SEH-rah-tops).

Continue these two trails of dinosaur prints up the page.

OCEAN MONSTER

Paint a line of prints to create this undersea predator.

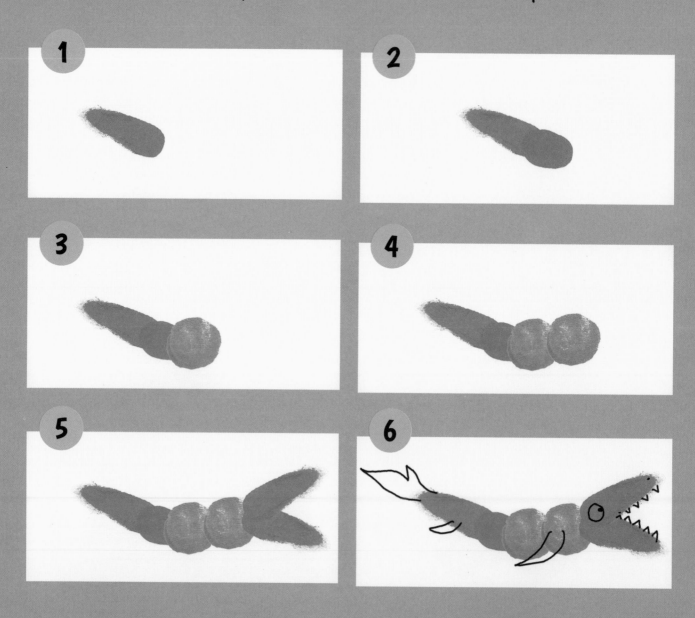

MOSASAURUS (MOZZ-ah-SORE-us)

Add a fingerprint pattern to this fierce hunter.
Then, print lots of fish for it to swim after!

Like this!

STRANGE SKULL

This odd-looking dino has a large crest on its head.

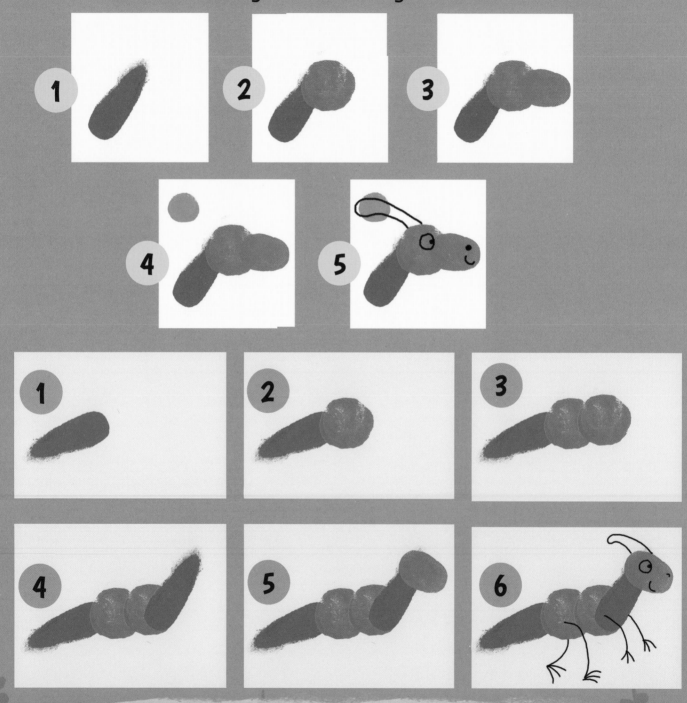

PARASAUROLOPHUS (PA-ra-sore-ROL-off-us)

LiTTLE NiPPER

Give this tiny flyer a long tail and sharp teeth!

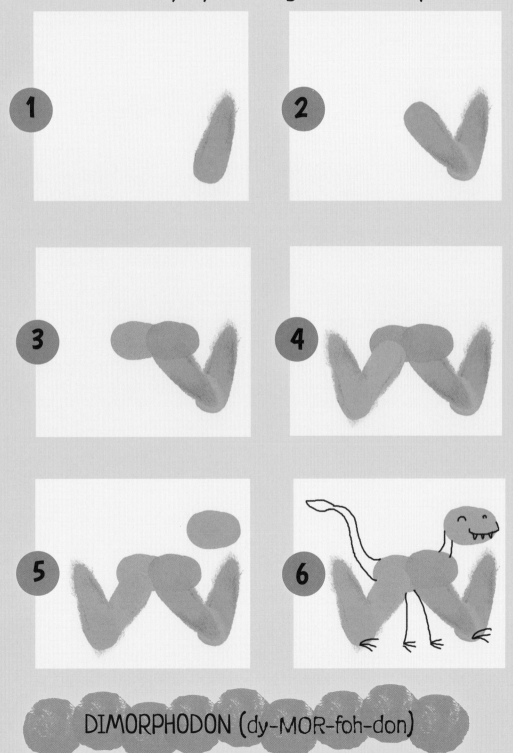

DIMORPHODON (dy-MOR-foh-don)

UNDERSEA SPEEDSTER

Add fins and a long nose to this swift sea predator.

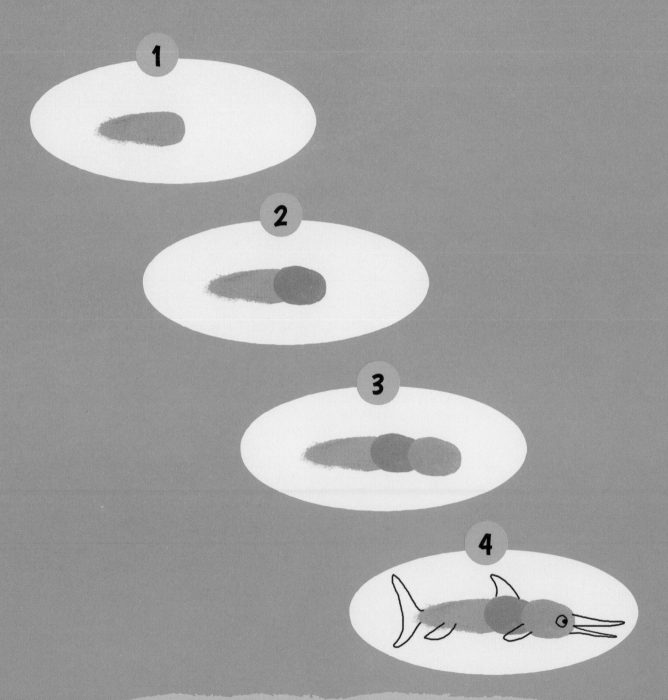

ICHTHYOSAURUS (ICK-thee-oh-SORE-us)

Watch out! Can you print two or more fast predators swimming after the fish?

REACHING HiGH

You'll need lots of fingertip prints for this dino's long neck!

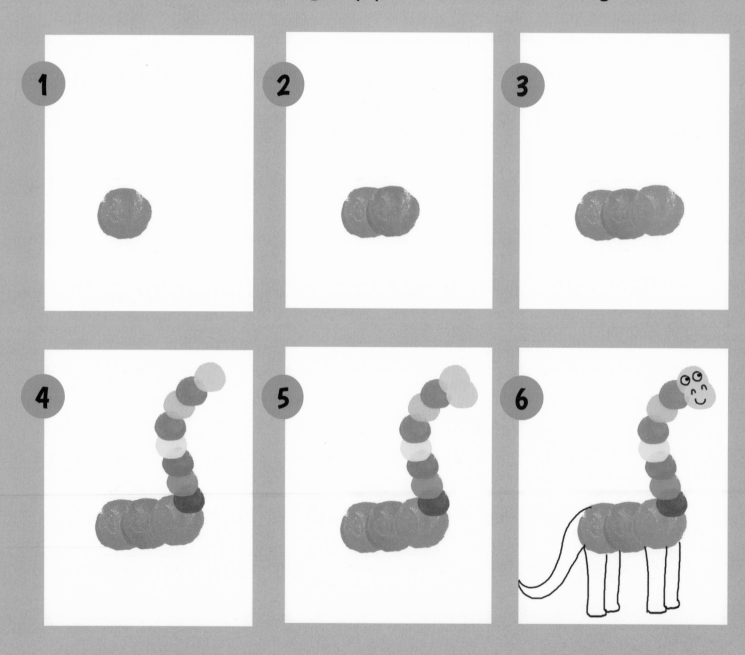

BRACHIOSAURUS (BRACK-ee-oh-SORE-us)

SPLENDID SHELL

Give this early turtle an eye-catching shell.

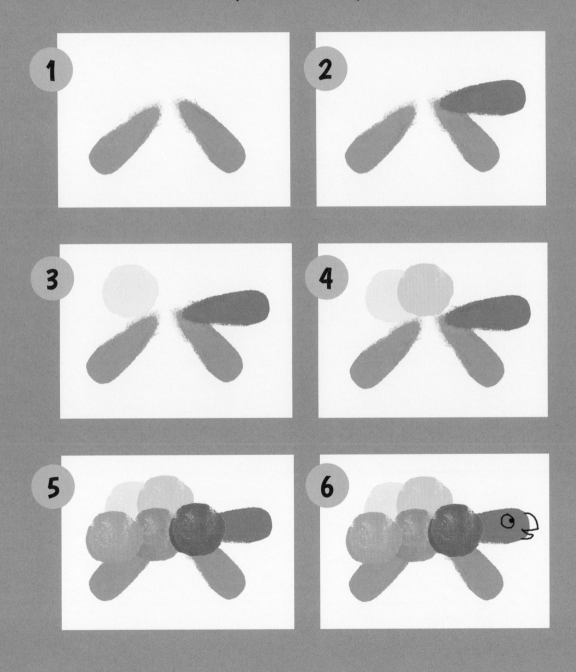

ARCHELON (ARK-eh-lon)

FiNE FEATHERS

Follow the steps to create this feathered friend.

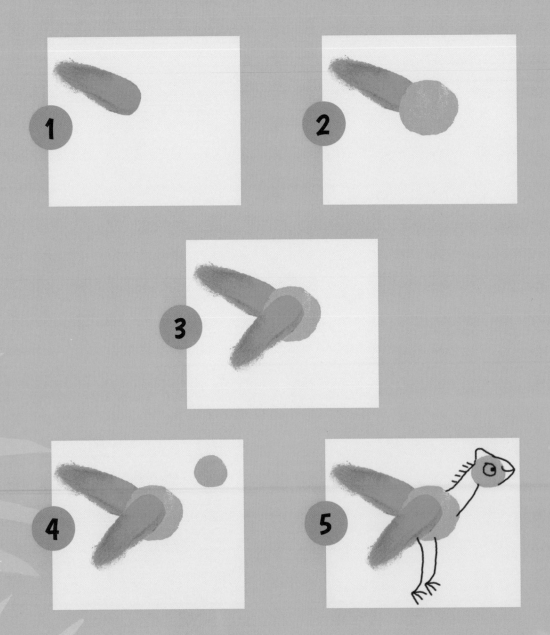

OVIRAPTOR (OH-vee-RAP-tor)

Add smudges to the raptor's head for a feathery crest.
Then, add fingerprint feathers to its body, too.

SEA SCORPiON

This undersea snapper needs many legs and claws.

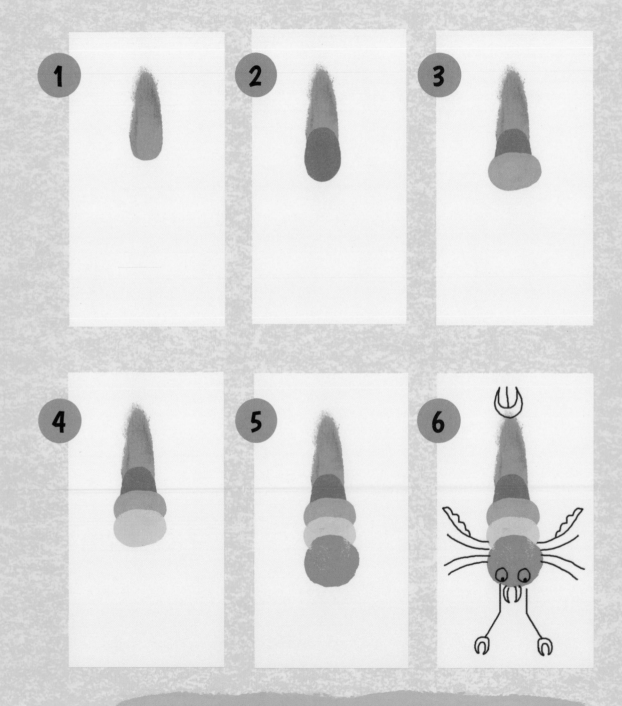

PTEROGOTUS (TEH-roh-GOAT-us)

DRINKING DINOS

Make the reflections match the dinosaurs!

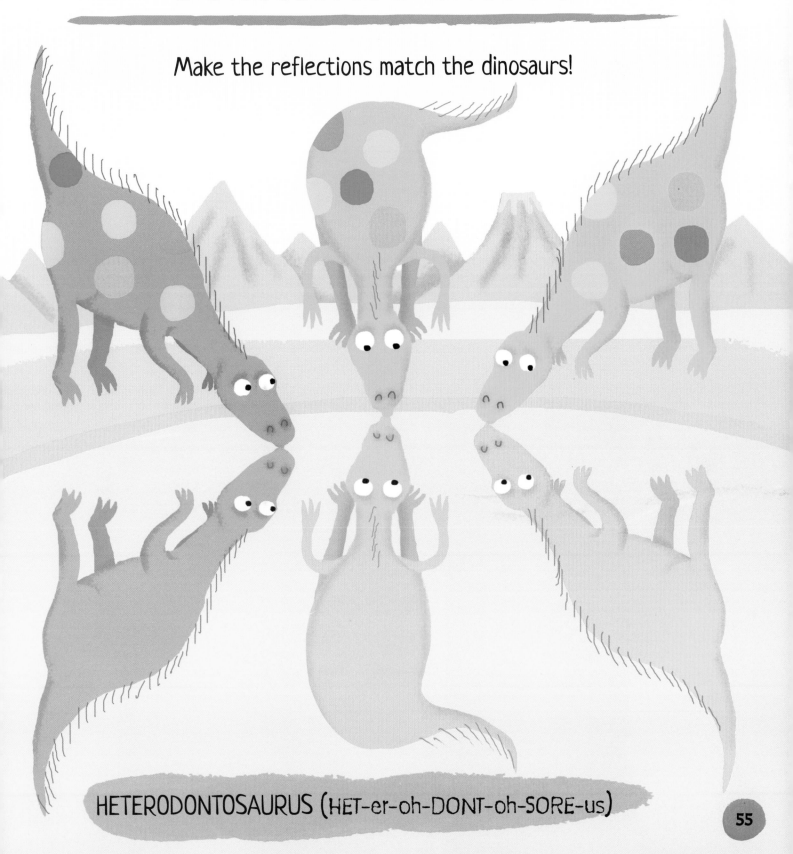

HETERODONTOSAURUS (HET-er-oh-DONT-oh-SORE-us)

SPIKY SPINES

Can you draw this prickly creature?

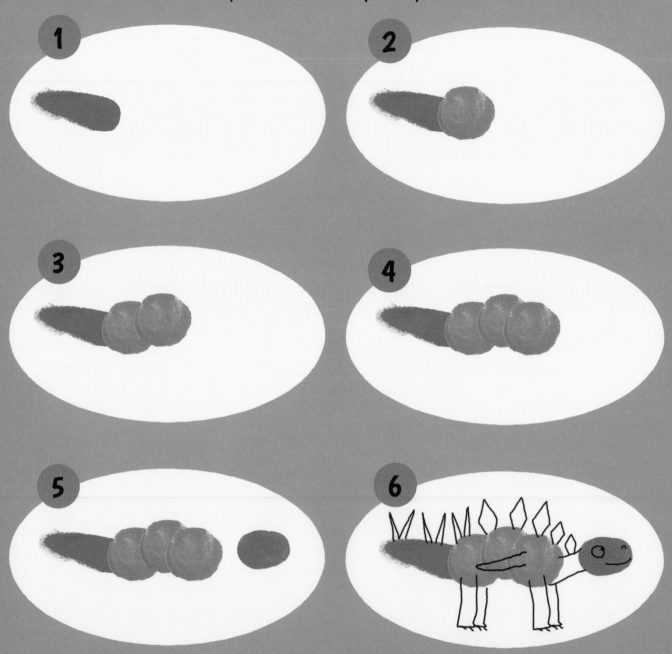

KENTROSAURUS (KEN-troh-SORE-us)

Complete this dino with fingerprint plates and smudge spikes.

SKY HiGH

Follow the steps to make this flying reptile.

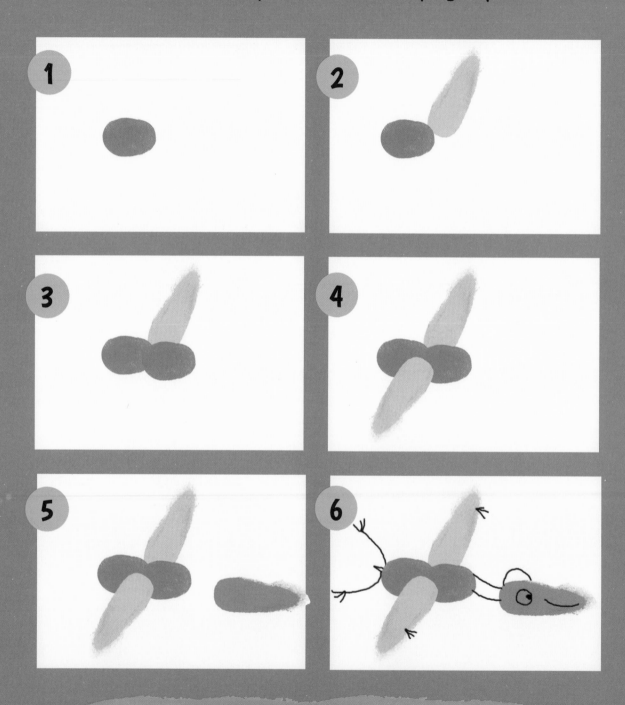

PTERODACTYLUS (TEH-ro-DACK-tih-lus)

Add more prehistoric flyers gliding above the water, hunting for fish.

PLANT PECKER

Can you paint this beaky dino?

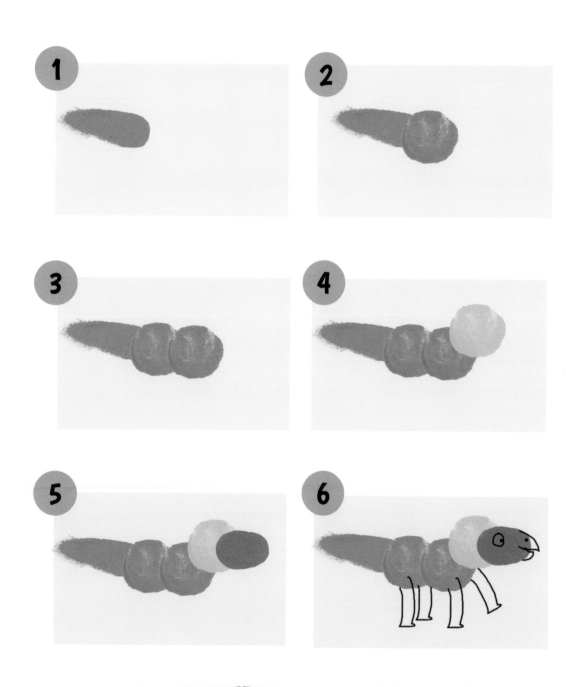

1

2

3

4

5

6

PROTOCERATOPS (PRO-toh-SEH-rah-tops)

HiGH REACHERS

This treetop feeder needs a row of smudge spines on its neck, back, and tail. Add more leaves to the trees, too!

BAROSAURUS (BARE-oh-SORE-us)

FAST FOOTER

This speedy dinosaur needs long legs to race away!

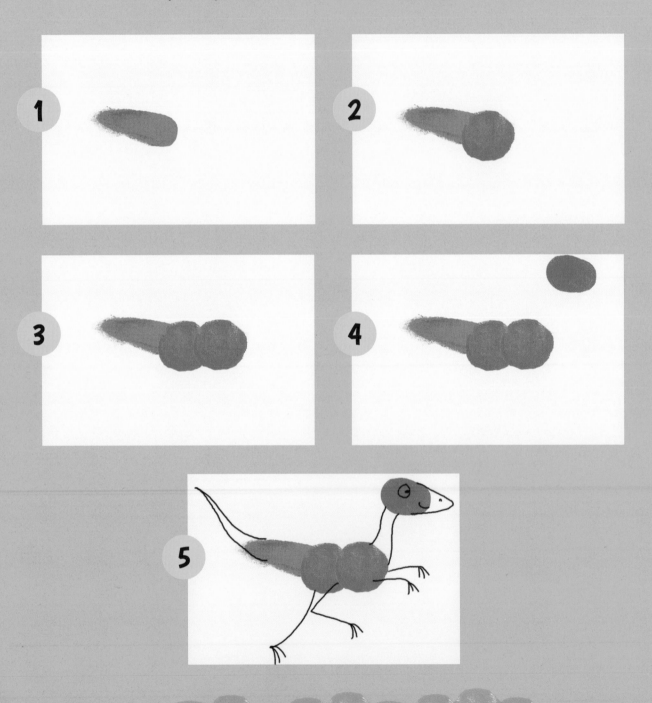

GALLIMIMUS (GAL-lee-MEEM-us)

CROWNING GLORY

Give the dinos head crests and spotted skin.

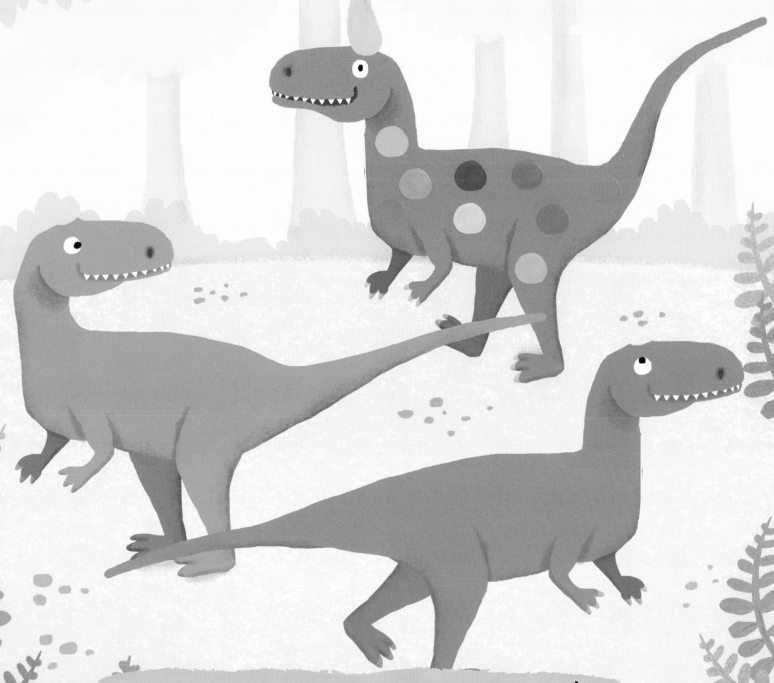

CRYOLOPHOSAURUS (CRY-oh-LOFF-oh-SORE-us)

BLEACHED BONES

Dip your fingers in white paint for this dino bone ...

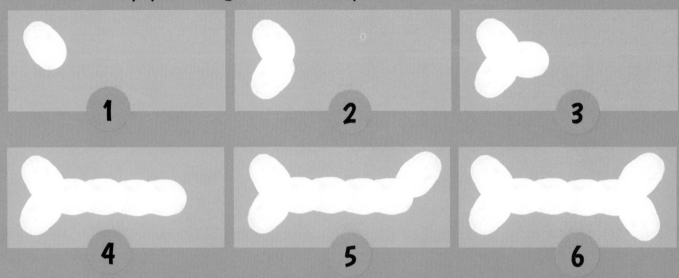

Next, try the neck bones and skull ...

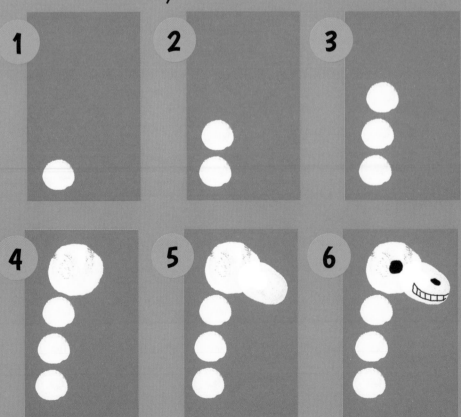

Now, add some bones to this fun fossil to build
a complete dinosaur!

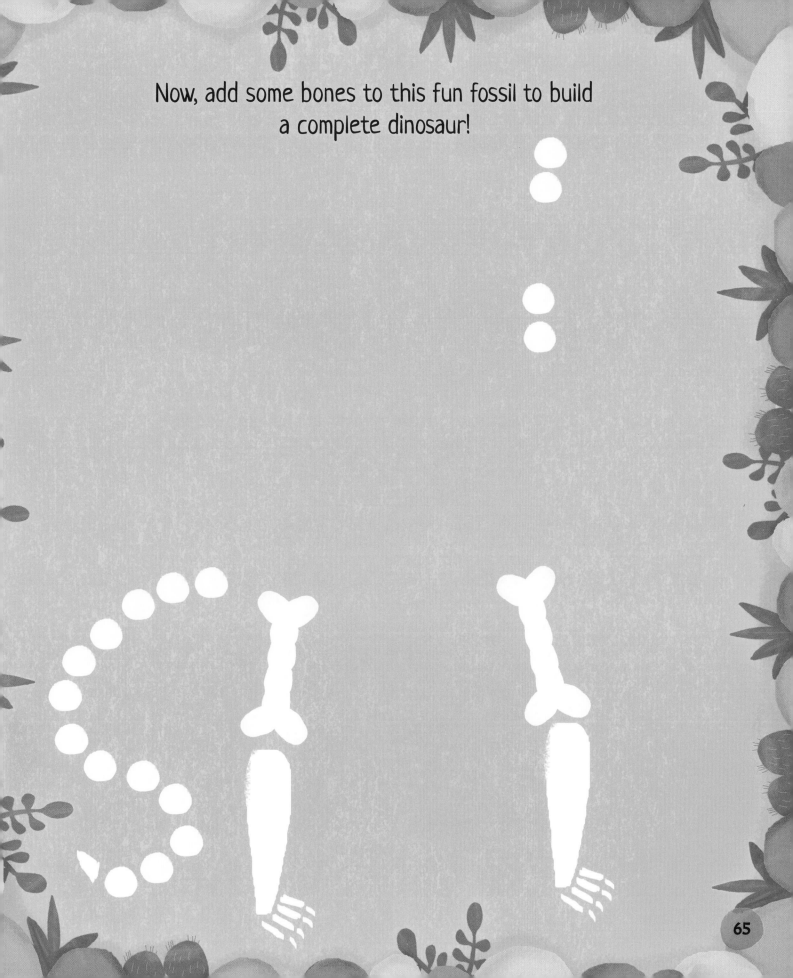

WILD WINGS

Join two handprints for this ancient bird's wings.

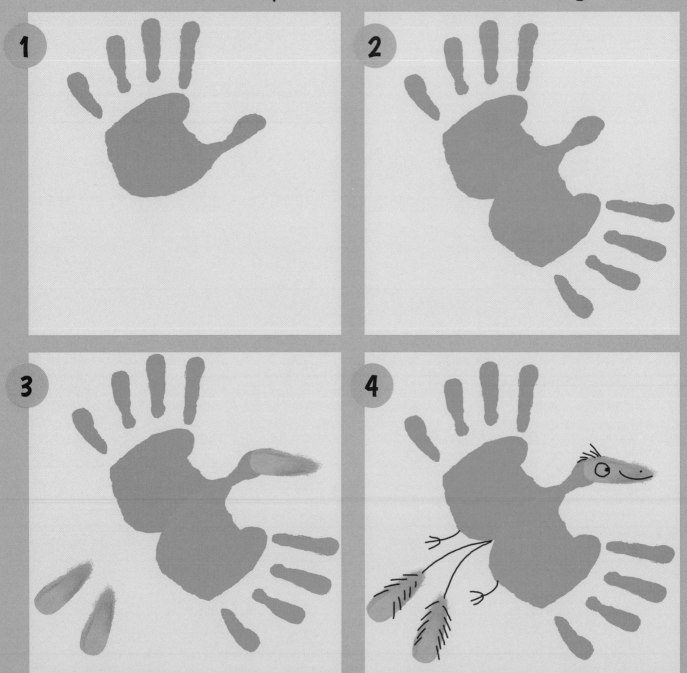

CONFUSIUSORNIS (KON-few-shu-SORE-niss)

Now, add your prehistoric birds flying through the swampy jungle!

EGG THIEVES

This dino is known for stealing eggs!

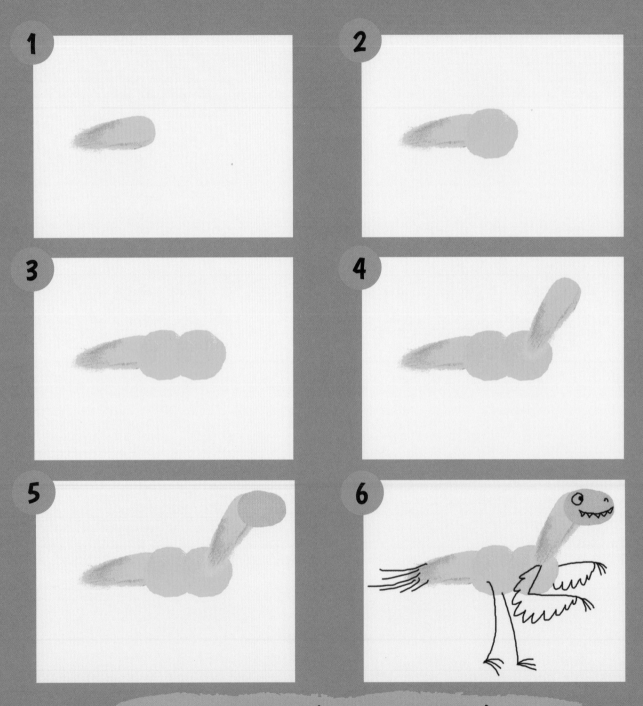

UTAHRAPTOR (YOO-tah-RAP-tor)

Add more feathers to these sneaky creatures, plus extra fingerprint eggs to the nest for them to take.

SCISSOR CLAWS

This beaked dinosaur has very long claws!

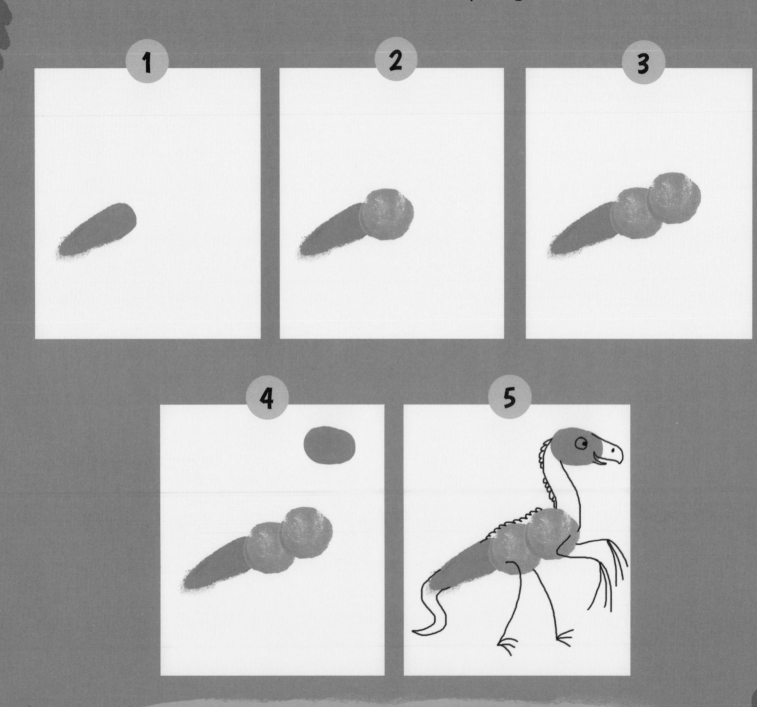

THERIZINOSAURUS (THEH-rih-ZEEN-oh-SORE-us)

HORNED HEAD

Complete the spiky shield around this horned dino's head.

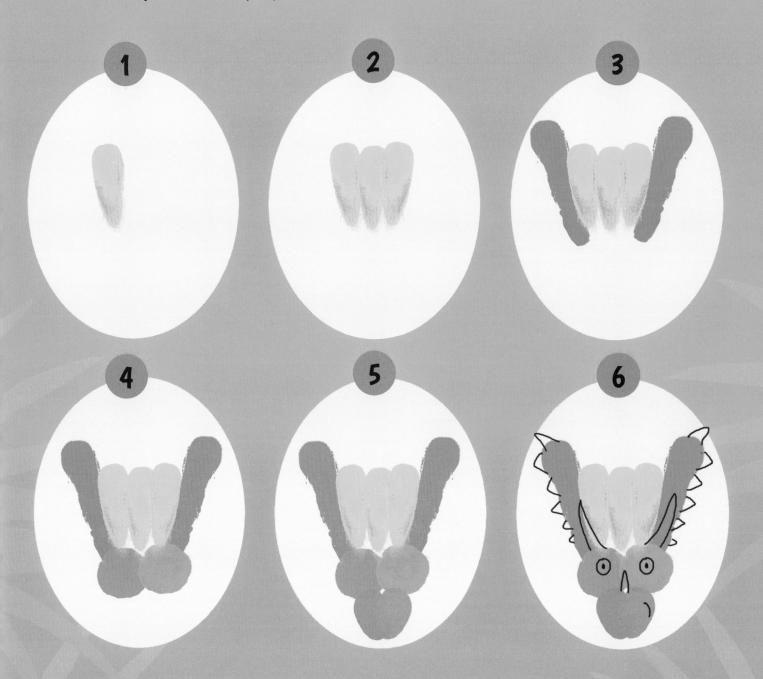

PENTACERATOPS (PENT-ah-SER-ah-tops)

TICKLY TENTACLES

Can you make a shell for this squid-like creature?

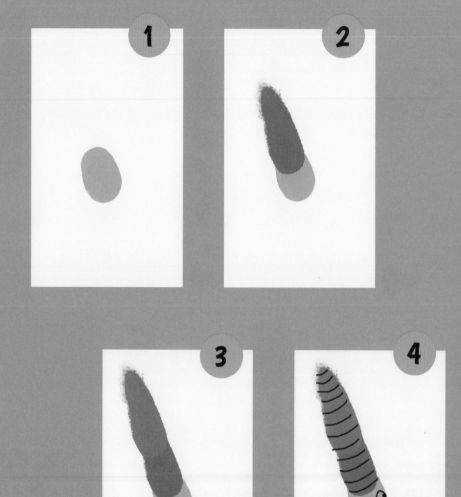

CAMEROCERAS (CAM-eh-roh-SEH-ras)

Paint strings of fingerprints to give these sea creatures their tentacles.

HORNED HUNTER

This two-horned hunter looks a bit like a monster!

CARNOTAURUS (KAR-noh-TORE-us)

TALL SAILS

Add rows of fingerprints to give this dino a tall sail on its back.

SPINOSAURUS (SPINE-oh-SORE-us)

POINTY PROTECTION

This plant-eater is covered with bony spines!

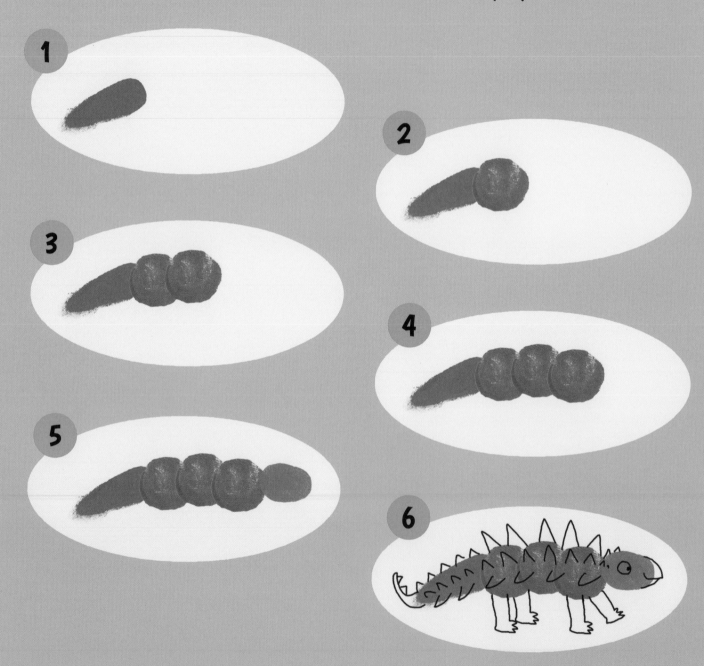

GASTONIA (gas-TOH-nee-ah)

Can you use lots of paints to cover this dinosaur's back with spikes?

QUIRKY QUILLS

It's easy to create this parrot-like dino!

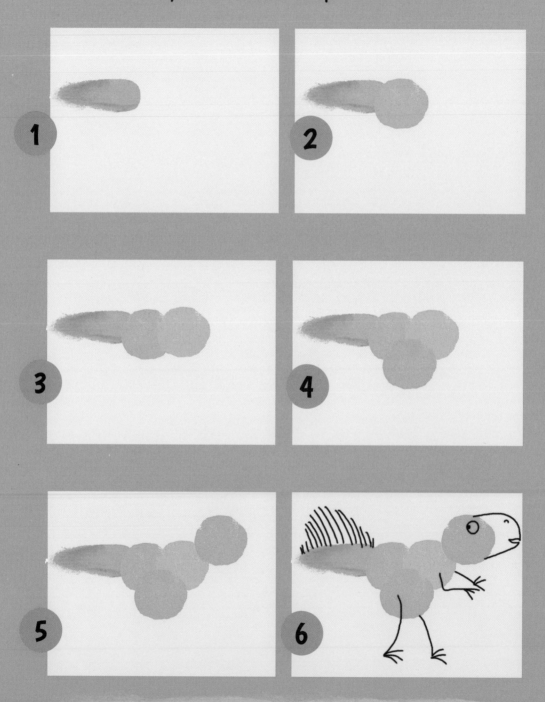

PSITTACOSAURUS (SIT-ak-oh-SORE-us)

Add fingertip skin patterns and a handprint for quills on the large dinosaur.

HEAVY BEAST

Use a row of fingerprints for the gigantic dino's body.

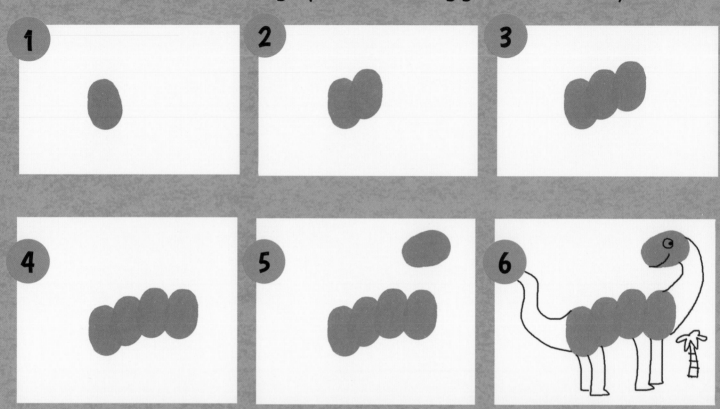

Now, build a palm tree with finger smudges.

ARGENTINOSAURUS (AR-juhn-TEE-no-SORE-us)

Plant more palm trees for this enormous dinosaur
to tower over.

PADDLING PREDATOR

Can you paint this long sea creature?

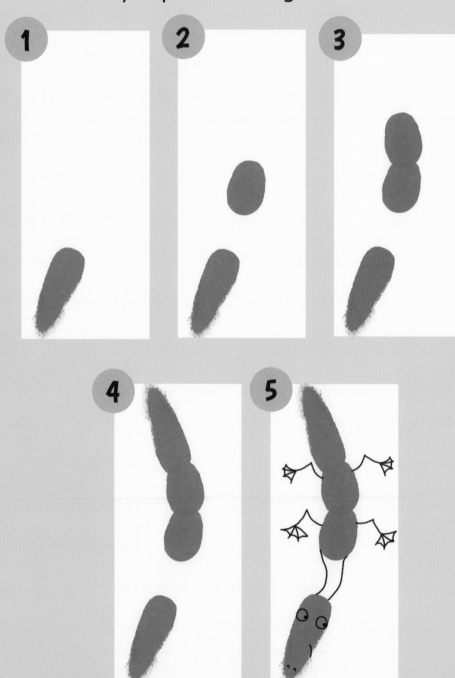

NOTHOSAURUS (NO-toe-SORE-us)

Add finger-smudge patterns on the body of this undersea hunter.
Then, dip your thumb in white paint to add bubbles in the water!

FLAPPING FEATHERS

Add a feathery tail to this birdlike dinosaur.

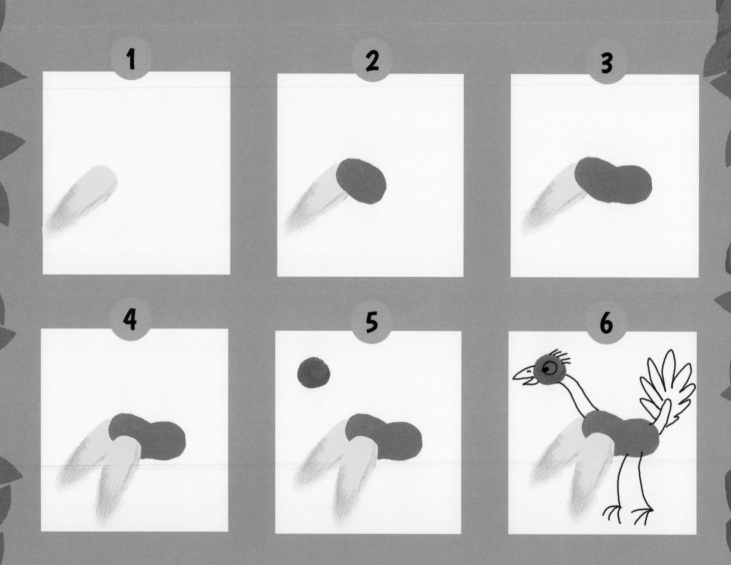

1

2

3

4

5

6

CAUDIPTERYX (caw-DIP-teh-riks)

Use loads of fingerprints to add bright feathers
to the dino arms and tails.

FANCY FiNS

Add a spiny sail along the back of this long dino.

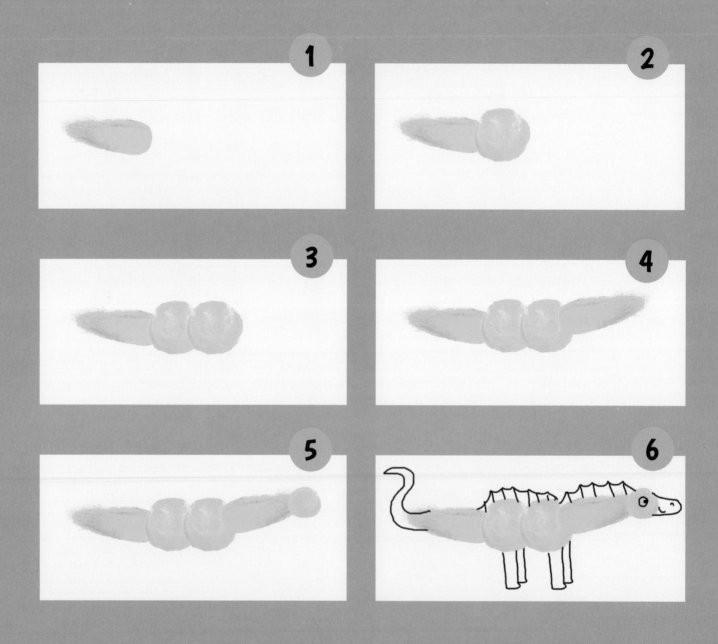

AMARGASAURUS (ah-MARG-ah-SORE-us)

Paint all over this dino's neck and back. Then, add some fingertip and thumb spots to its skin as well!

FANTASTIC FOSSIL

Follow the steps to build this dino skeleton.

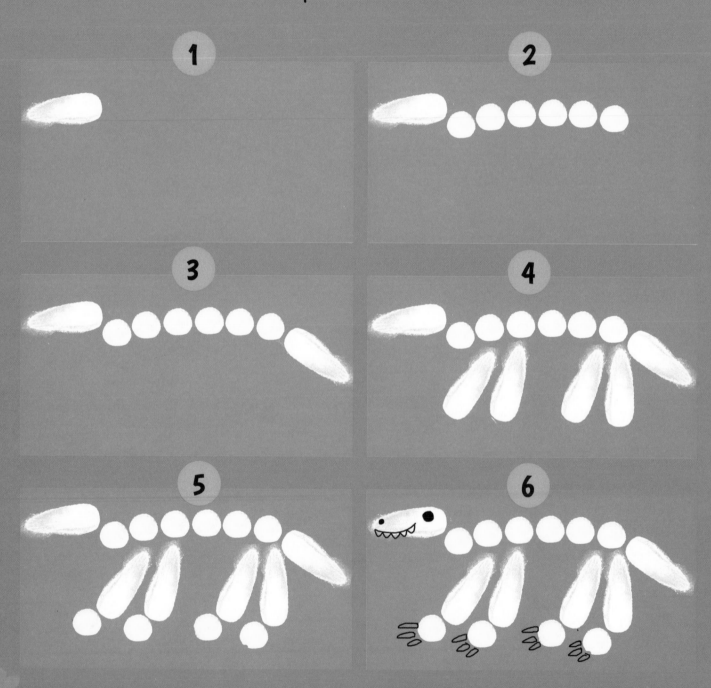

Now, print a whole underground fossil, ready to be discovered by dinosaur experts!

FLYING FRIGHT

Use two pointed smudges for this flying reptile's toothy jaws.

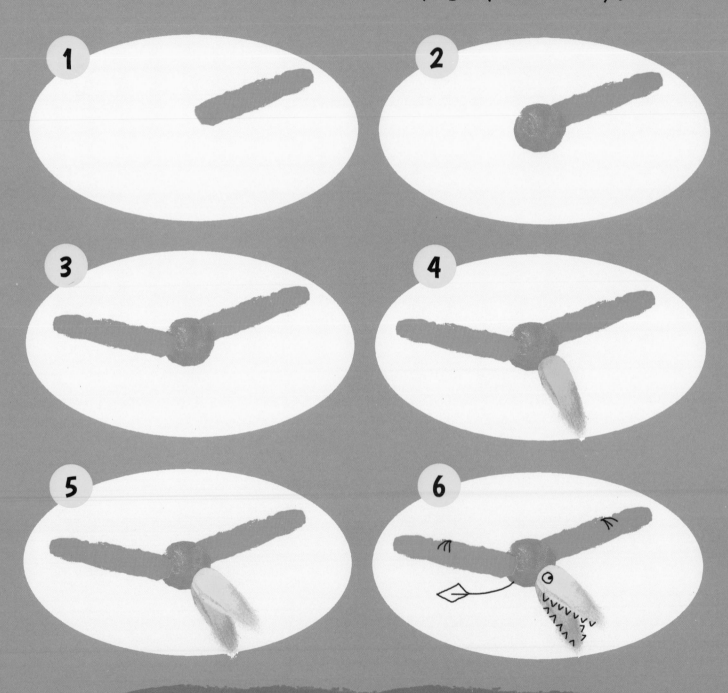

RHAMPHORHYNCHUS (RAM-foh-RINK-us)

Fill the sky with gliding reptiles. Give them long wings and rows of sharp teeth!

FiERCE FANGS

Give this biter a long tongue, spotted skin, and a toothy grin!

ALBERTOSAURUS (al-BERT-oh-SORE-us)

GUSHING LAVA

Make the volcano erupt with yellow and red fingerprint splashes.

UP HiGH

Connect the prints to show a sauropod from above.

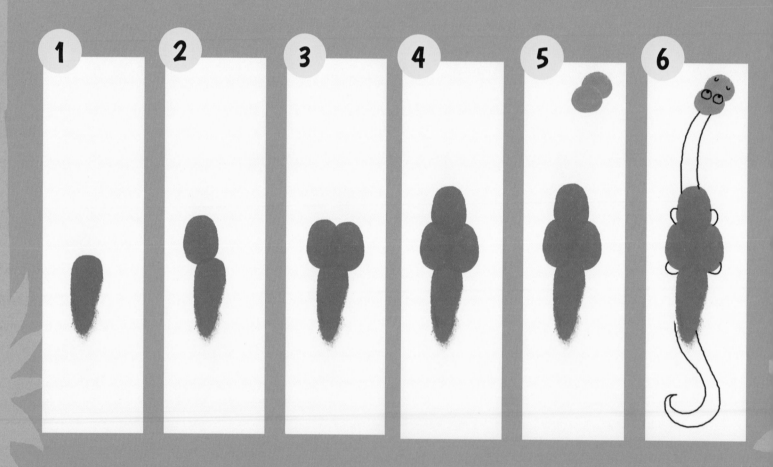

CAMARASAURUS (KAM-ah-ra-SORE-us)

Add several more sauropods approaching the water.

CLEVER CLAW

Use the side of your hand and fingers to make this dino claw.

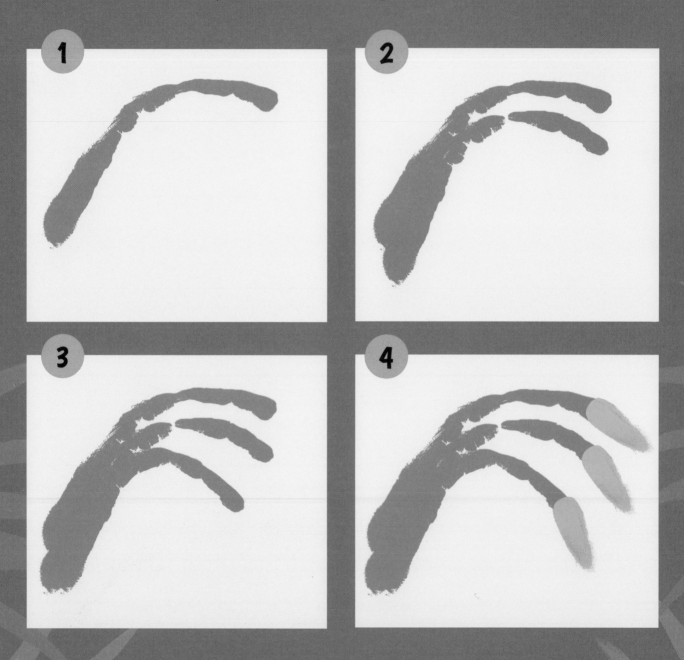